Addition and Subtraction

Bath · New York · Cologne · Melbourne · Delhi
Hong Kong · Shenzhen · Singapore

Helping your child

- The activities in this book will help your child to learn about addition and subtraction. Pictures provide hints and clues to support your child's calculations.

- Your child will gain the confidence to: add and subtract to and from two-digit numbers; use addition and subtraction bonds; use repeated addition as a method of multiplying; understand the +, −, x and = symbols; and calculate the value of an unknown number within a number sentence.

- Your child will learn about doubles and halves, odd and even numbers, and two- and three-digit numbers.

- Set aside time to do the activities together. Do a little at a time, so that your child enjoys learning.

- Give lots of encouragement and praise. Use the gold stars as rewards and incentives.

- The answers are on page 32.

This edition published by Parragon Books Ltd in 2017

Parragon Books Ltd
Chartist House
15-17 Trim Street
Bath BA1 1HA, UK
www.parragon.com

Copyright © Parragon Books Ltd 2009–2017

Written by Paul Broadbent
Illustrated by Adam Linley
Cover illustrated by Simon Abbot
Educational Consultant: Christine Vaughan

ISBN: 978-1-4748-7793-0

Printed in China

Contents

Counting on

Use the number line to count on. Show the jumps and write the answers. The first one has been done for you.

12 + 3 = 15

10 11 12 13 14 15 16 17 18 19

8 + 4 = ☐

6 7 8 9 10 11 12 13 14 15

7 + 7 = ☐

7 8 9 10 11 12 13 14 15 16

Complete the sums below.

9 + 6 = ☐   13 + 4 = ☐   15 + 5 = ☐

11 + 10 = ☐   16 + 13 = ☐   20 + 20 = ☐

32 + 21 = ☐   55 + 27 = ☐

Counting back

Show the jumps and write the answers.

$14 - 5 = \boxed{}$

6 7 8 9 10 11 12 13 14 15 16 17

$18 - 6 = \boxed{}$

9 10 11 12 13 14 15 16 17 18 19 20

$16 - 7 = \boxed{}$

7 8 9 10 11 12 13 14 15 16 17 18

Complete the sums below.

$10 - 4 = \boxed{}$ $13 - 5 = \boxed{}$ $11 - 3 = \boxed{}$

$14 - 13 = \boxed{}$ $19 - 11 = \boxed{}$ $20 - 10 = \boxed{}$

$46 - 25 = \boxed{}$ $63 - 37 = \boxed{}$

Note for parent: Your child will be familiar with counting back as a method of taking away and developing mental subtraction skills at this age.

5

Making totals

Count each set. Write the totals.

☐ + ☐ = ☐

☐ + ☐ = ☐

☐ + ☐ = ☐

☐ + ☐ = ☐

Note for parent: This activity gives your child practice in combining sets to make totals.

Draw snowflakes to make the totals.

$$6 + \boxed{} = 10$$

$$5 + \boxed{} = 12$$

$$\boxed{} + 3 = 10$$

Join pairs of numbers that total 12.

Taking away

Cross out four items on each shelf.
Write how many are left.

6 – 4 = ☐

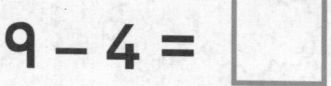

9 – 4 = ☐

☐ **– 4 =** ☐

☐ **– 4 =** ☐

Cross out five in each set. Write how many are left.

☐ **– 5 =** ☐

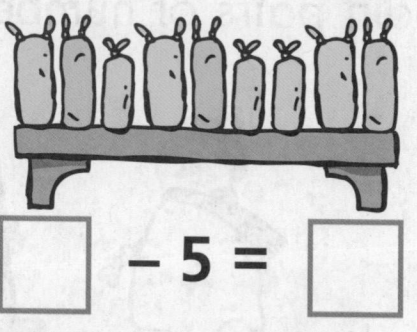

☐ **– 5 =** ☐

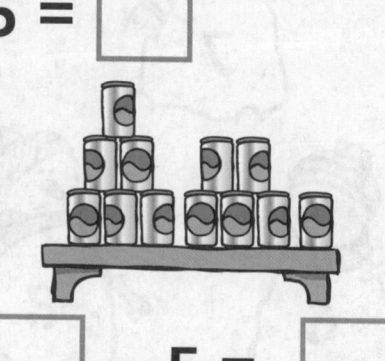

☐ **– 5 =** ☐

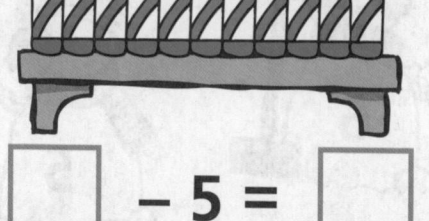

☐ **– 5 =** ☐

Note for parent: This activity gives your child practice in subtraction by taking amounts away.

Coco the clown has 12 balloons. Write the new totals in the boxes.

Sam buys
3 balloons.

12 – 3 = ☐

Coco loses
1 balloon.

9 – 1 = ☐

Lucy buys
5 balloons.

8 – 5 = ☐

Coco gives
2 balloons away.

3 – 2 = ☐

Number machines

Total the numbers going into the machines.

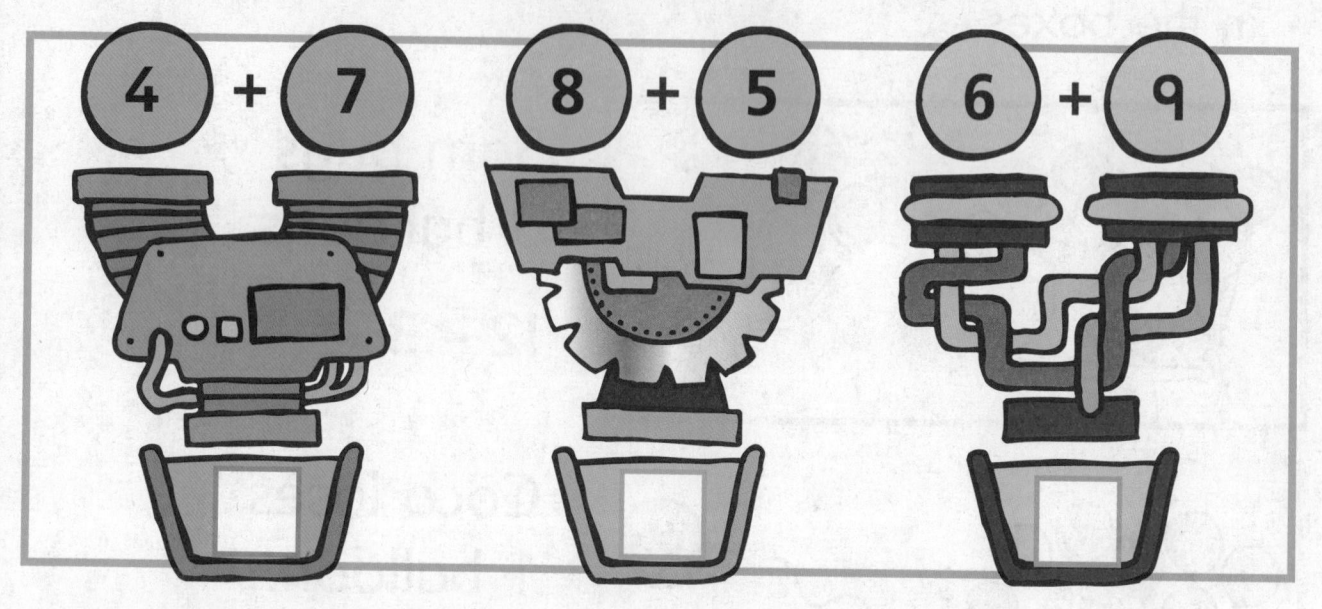

Write the numbers coming out of this machine.

Note for parent: Ask your child to look at the numbers going into each machine and work out the numbers coming out mentally, rather than counting on their fingers, for example.

Write the numbers coming out of these machines.

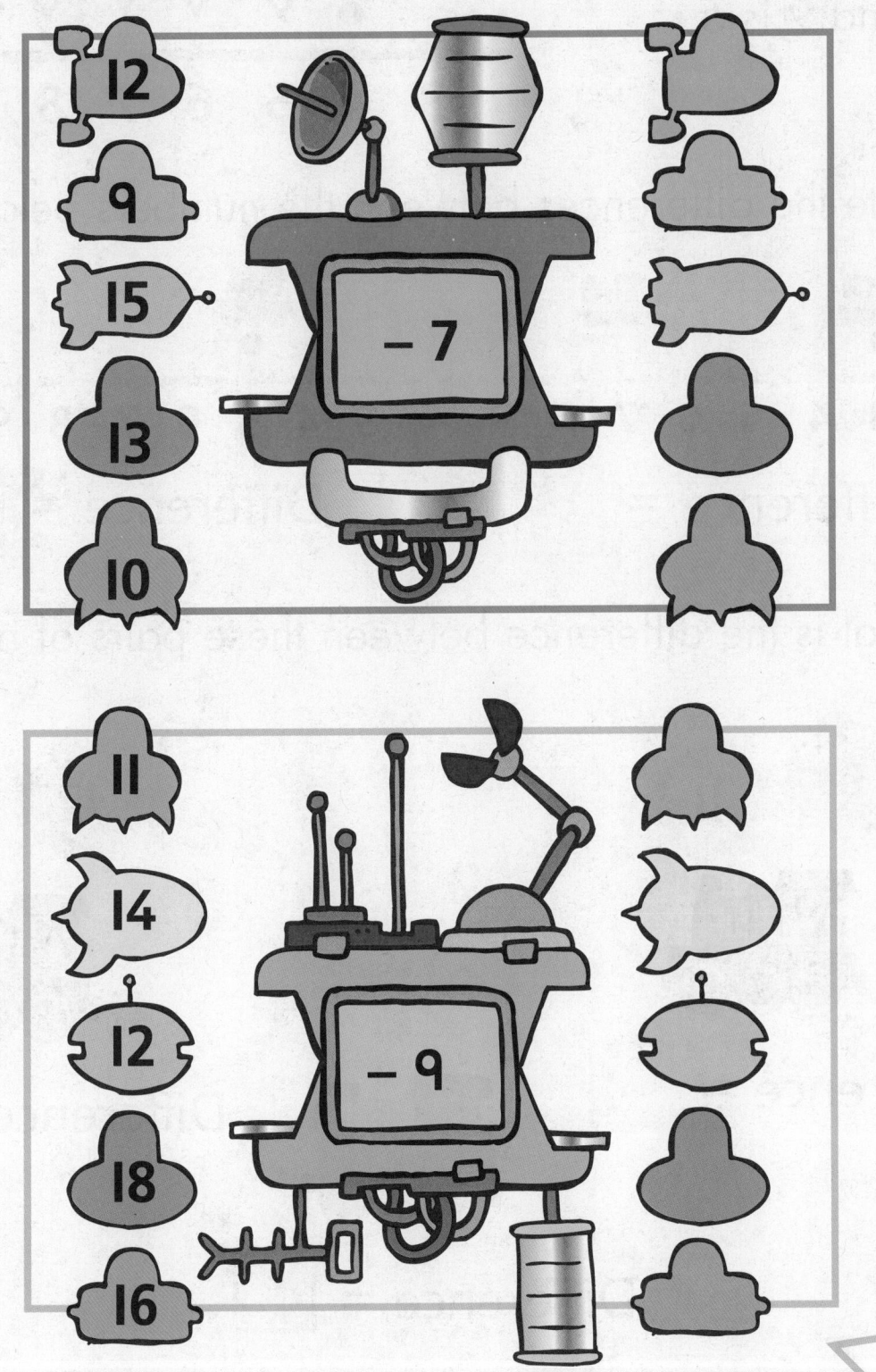

Note for parent: Ask your child to write out some of the sums from these pages on a separate piece of paper, using the +, − and = symbols.

11

Differences

The difference between 4 and 9 is 5.

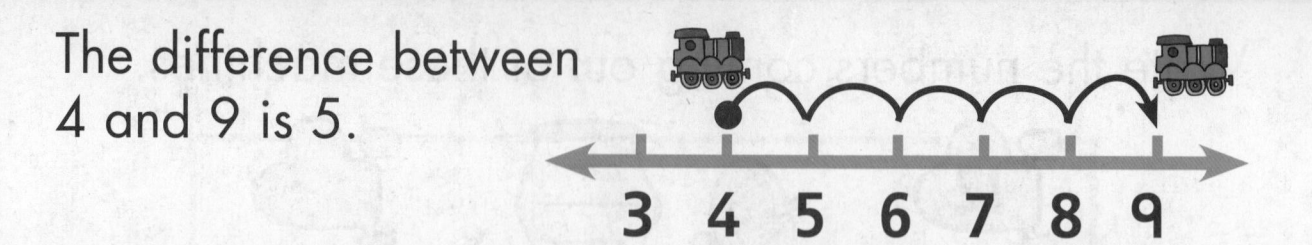

Write the differences between the numbers below.

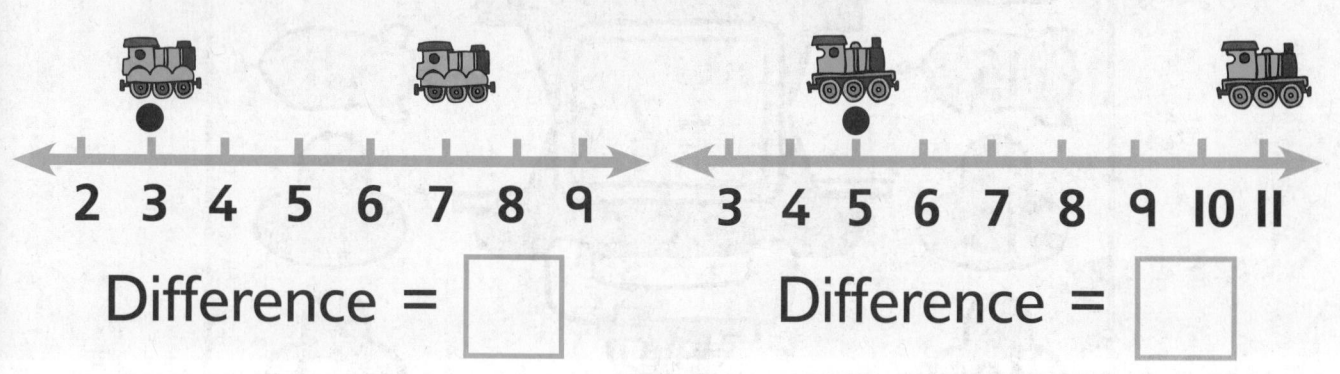

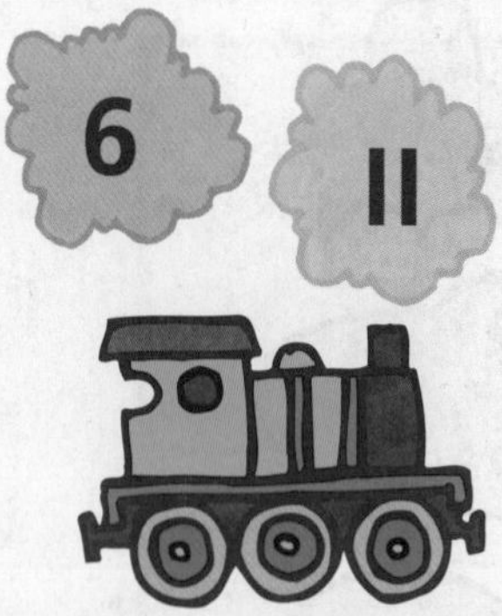

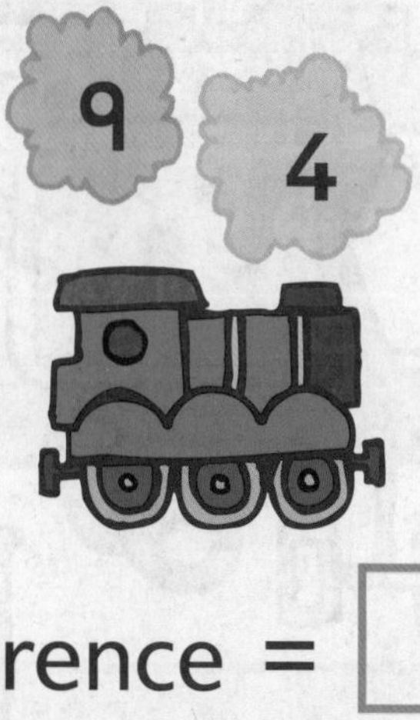

Difference = ☐

Difference = ☐

What is the difference between these pairs of numbers?

6   11

Difference = ☐

9   4

Difference = ☐

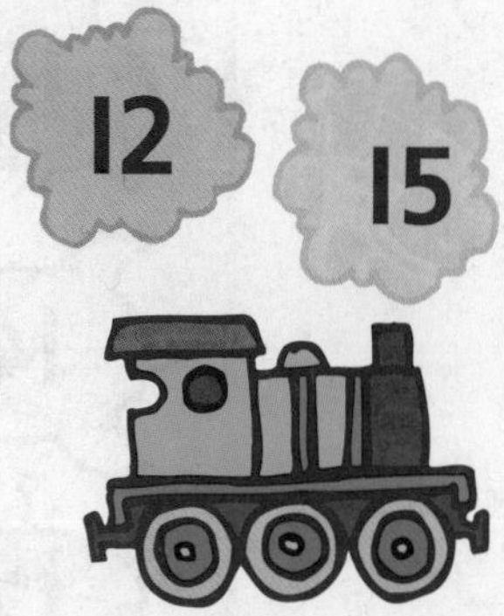

12   15

Difference = ☐

Find the pairs of numbers with a difference of 6.
Colour each matching pair.

Fill in the missing number so that each submarine has a difference of 5. The first one has been done for you.

Addition bonds

Make the totals in the middle of the spacestations in different ways. The first one has been done for you.

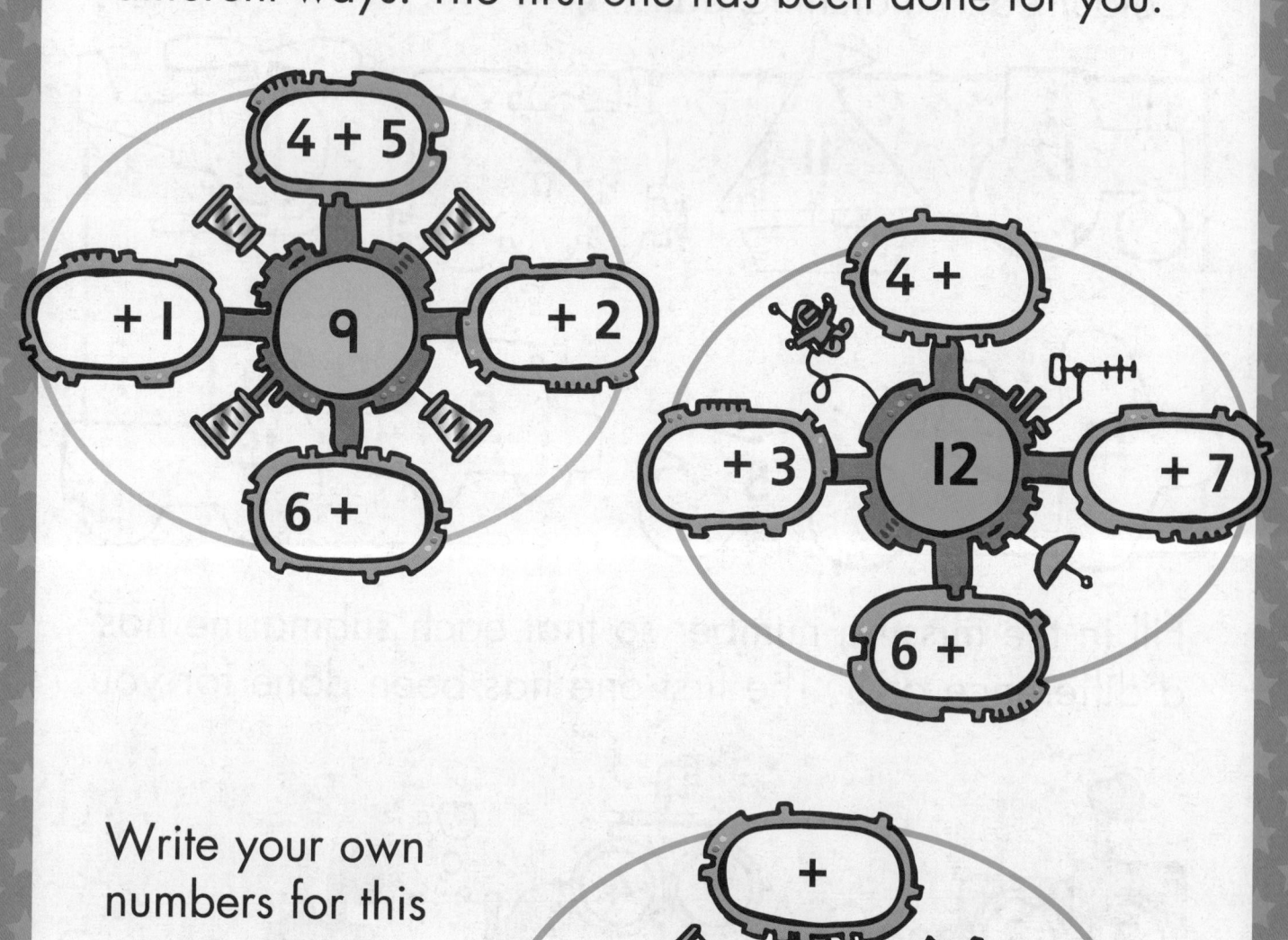

Write your own numbers for this spacestation.

Note for parent: Addition bonds are all the different ways that a total can be made with two numbers.

Quick quiz

Count each set. Write the total.

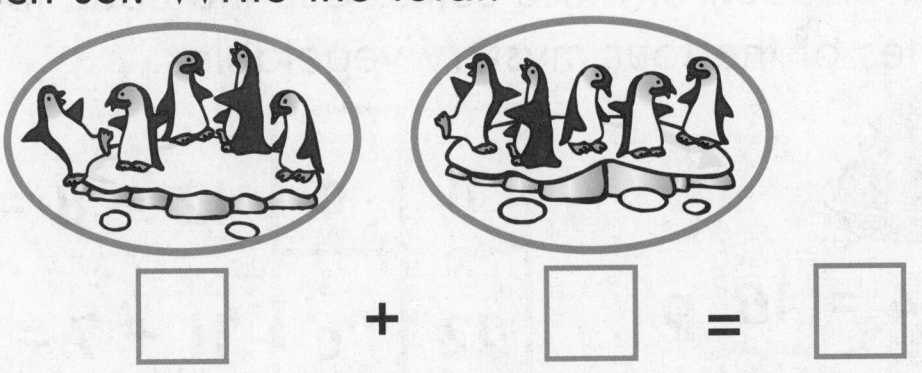

[ ] + [ ] = [ ]

Cross out four items on each shelf. Write how many are left.

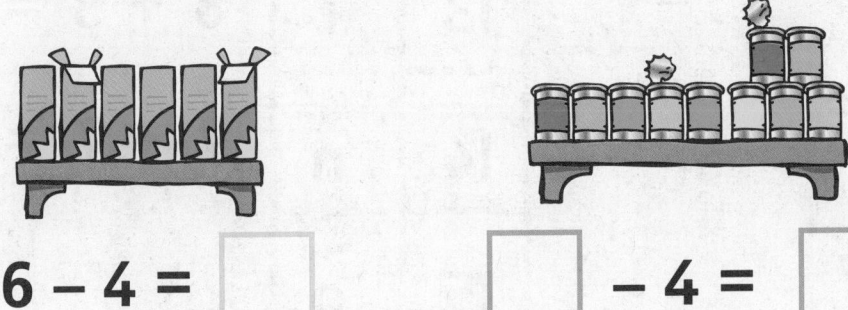

6 − 4 = [ ]   [ ] − 4 = [ ]

Write the numbers coming out of this machine.

11
14
12
18
16

− 9

Note for parent: This page is a chance to revise some of the learning so far.

15

Adding to 20

Answer each of these sums. Use the code to find the names of the four mystery vegetables.

11	a
12	c
13	i
14	n
15	o
16	p
17	r
18	e
19	t
20	b

12 + 4 = 16 p

9 + 9 = ___

6 + 5 = ___

7 + 5 = ___

2 + 9 = ___

10 + 7 = ___

8 + 9 = ___

9 + 6 = ___

10 + 9 = ___

12 + 8 = ___

11 + 7 = ___

8 + 3 = ___

7 + 7 = ___

8 + 8 = ___

11 + 4 = ___

12 + 7 = ___

6 + 5 = ___

5 + 14 = ___

8 + 7 = ___

Note for parent: Ask your child how he or she worked out each answer.

Fill in the missing numbers to complete these addition walls. The first one has been done for you.

Write the numbers to complete these adding chains. The first answer has been done for you.

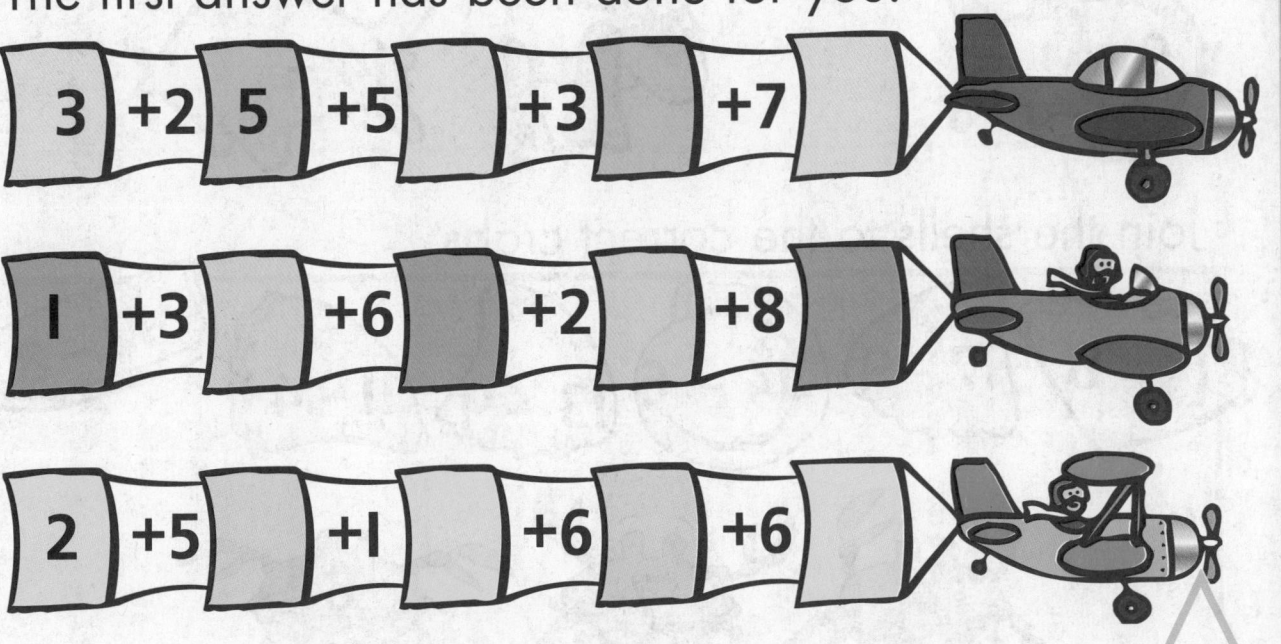

Subtraction bonds

Find the different ways of making 5.

Find the different ways of making 6.

Join the shells to the correct crabs.

Note for parent: Children generally find subtraction bonds more difficult than addition bonds.

Circle the odd one out in each set.

13 – 6
18 – 9
15 – 8
14 – 7

11 – 3
15 – 7
14 – 8
13 – 5

11 – 5
12 – 6
15 – 9
17 – 9

Join the matching answers.

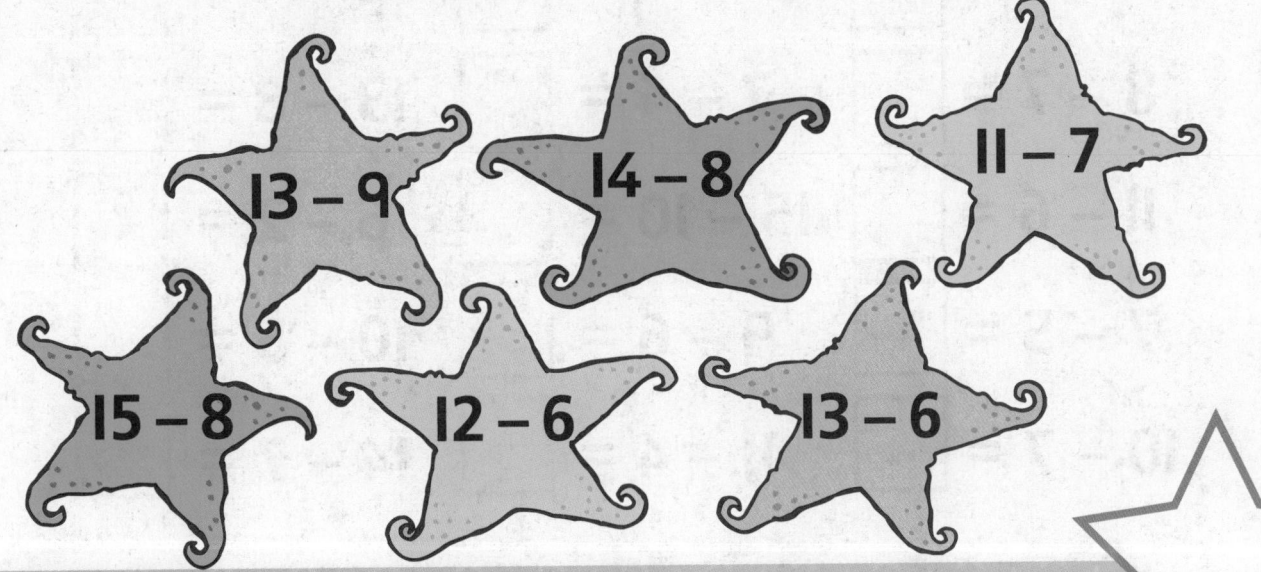

13 – 9
14 – 8
11 – 7
15 – 8
12 – 6
13 – 6

Note for parent: If your child knows that 5 + 7 = 12, then they can work out that 12 – 7 = 5.
Ask your child to write out any bonds they struggle with in this way.

19

Take away facts

Write the answers to these in words. Find the mystery number in the shaded squares.

14 – 7 →

11 – 6 →

13 – 7 →

17 – 5 →

13 – 5 →

16 – 15 →

16 – 7 →

Answer these as quickly as you can.
Time yourself and try to beat your best time.

9 – 4 = ☐   12 – 6 = ☐   8 – 4 = ☐

8 – 7 = ☐   7 – 4 = ☐   13 – 8 = ☐

11 – 6 = ☐   15 – 10 = ☐   6 – 2 = ☐

7 – 5 = ☐   9 – 6 = ☐   10 – 5 = ☐

10 – 7 = ☐   11 – 4 = ☐   14 – 7 = ☐

Note for parent: These activities give practice in learning the subtraction facts within 20.

Fill in the missing numbers to make each total. The first one has been done for you.

9 – 6   11 – 8   3

– 4   10 –   5

– 2   14 –   6

11 –   – 9   4

Write in your own numbers to make the total.

–   –   7

Complete the number trails back to zero.

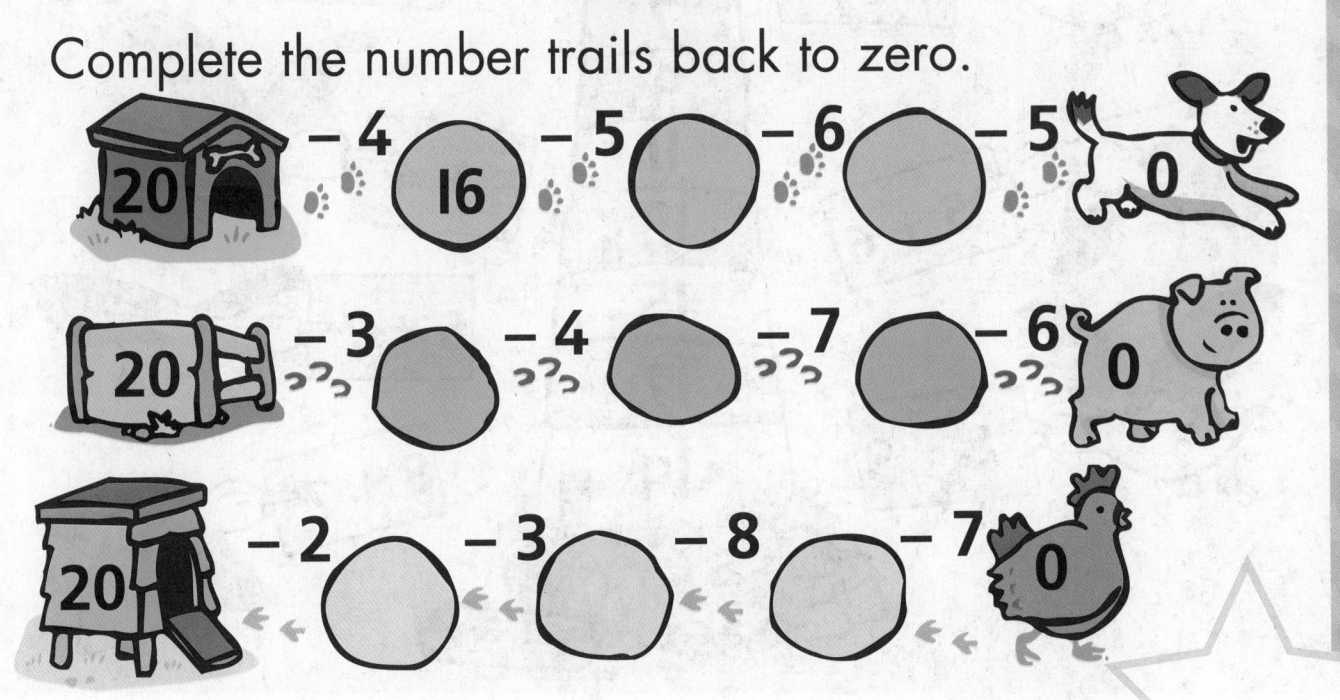

20   – 4   16   – 5   – 6   – 5   0

20   – 3   – 4   – 7   – 6   0

20   – 2   – 3   – 8   – 7   0

Doubles

Answer these doubles.

4 + 4 = ☐

6 + 6 = ☐

3 + 3 = ☐

5 + 5 = ☐

8 + 8 = ☐

2 + 2 = ☐

13 + 13 = ☐

10 + 10 = ☐

19 + 19 = ☐

Join the sums to the correct answers.

3 + 4

5 + 6

8 + 9

7
9
11
13
15
17
19

10 + 9

5 + 4

6 + 7

8 + 7

Note for parent: Ask your child if he or she can work out what half of each double is. You can also use doubles to work out 'near doubles', e.g. 6 + 6 is 12, so 6 + 7 is one more.

Repeated addition

Add the number in the circles together 3 times.
Write the total in the centre.
The first one has been completed for you.

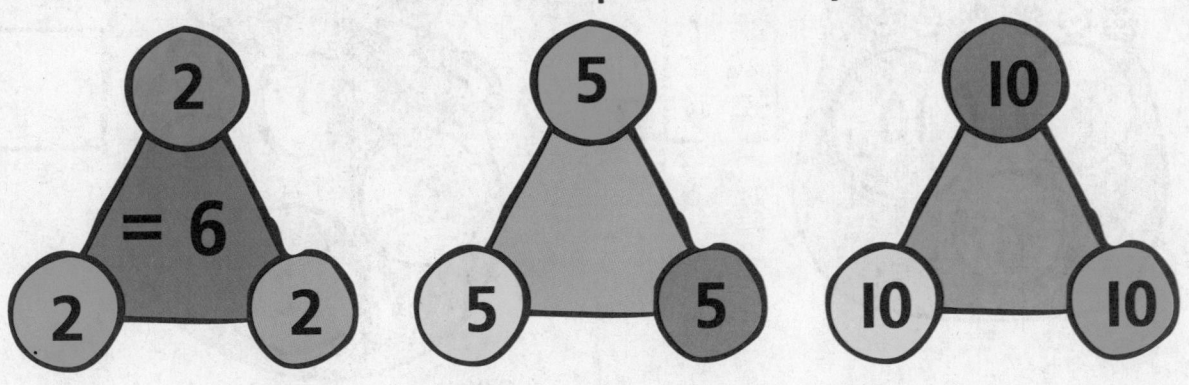

2 + 2 + 2 is the same as 2 x 3 = 6

Write the missing numbers below.

5 + 5 + ☐ = 5 x 3 = 15

10 + 10 + 10 = ☐ x 3 = ☐

2 + 2 + 2 + 2 = 2 x 4 = ☐

5 + ☐ + 5 + 5 + 5 = ☐ x 5 = 25

10 + 10 + 10 + 10 + 10 + 10 = 10 x ☐ = ☐

Note for parent: Repeated addition introduces the concept of multiplication and using the x symbol.
Ask your child to write out the calculations separately using the +, x and = symbols.

23

Money totals

How much money is in each purse? Write the answers in the boxes.

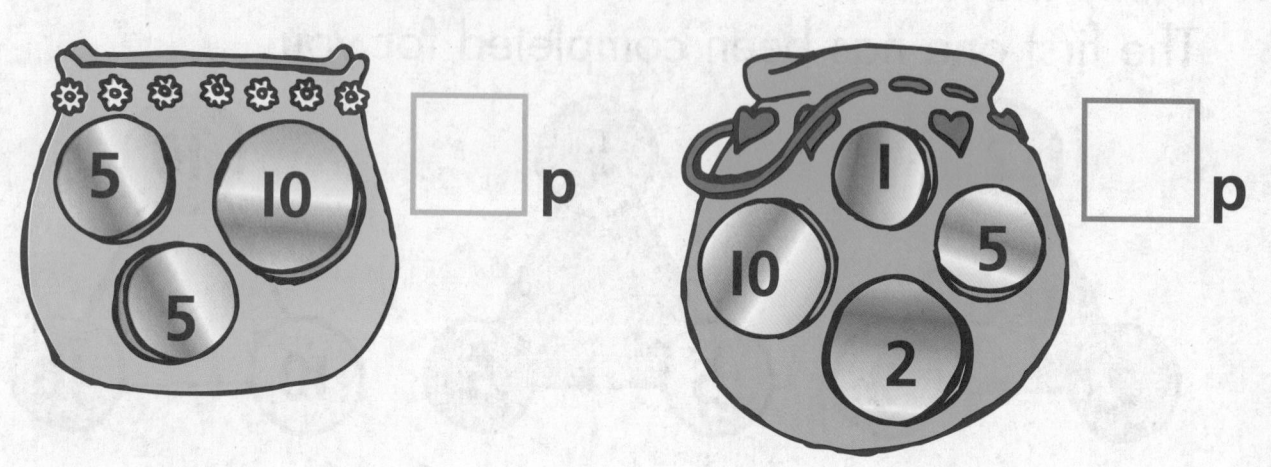

☐ p

☐ p

What is the total cost of each group of items?
Write the answers in the boxes.

£ ☐

£ ☐

£ ☐

Note for parent: This activity gives practice in totalling coins and exact pounds.

Giving change

Draw coins to show the change from 20p.
Write the amount of change.

7p [ ] [ ] p

8p [ ] [ ] p

12p [ ] [ ] p

15p [ ] [ ] p

Write the change from 20p for each of these.

11p change: [ ] p

14p change: [ ] p

6p change: [ ] p

9p change: [ ] p

16p change: [ ] p

Note for parent: To work out the amount of change your child needs to count on from the price up to 20p.

25

Hidden numbers

Leaves have hidden some of the numbers on the snakes. Write the missing numbers.

$8 + \text{\_} = 11$

$9 - \text{\_} = 5$

$\text{\_} - 6 = 6$

$\text{\_} + 6 = 13$

$\text{\_} + 12 = 25$

$23 + \text{\_} = 53$

$30 - \text{\_} = 3$

$\text{\_} - 15 = 9$

Work out the answers. Colour the even numbers red. Colour the odd numbers blue. Which number is hidden in the picture?

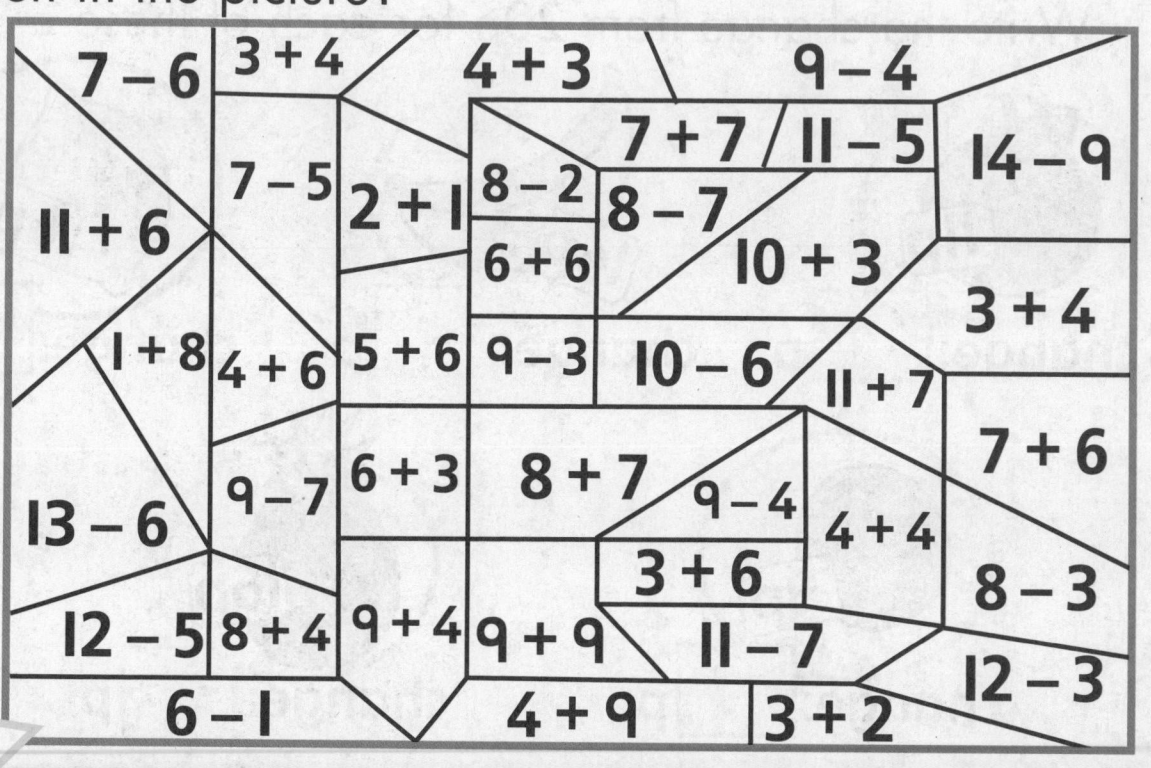

$7 - 6$ $3 + 4$ $4 + 3$ $9 - 4$

$7 + 7$ $11 - 5$ $14 - 9$

$11 + 6$ $7 - 5$ $2 + 1$ $8 - 2$ $8 - 7$

$6 + 6$ $10 + 3$

$3 + 4$

$1 + 8$ $4 + 6$ $5 + 6$ $9 - 3$ $10 - 6$ $11 + 7$

$7 + 6$

$13 - 6$ $9 - 7$ $6 + 3$ $8 + 7$ $9 - 4$ $4 + 4$

$3 + 6$ $8 - 3$

$12 - 5$ $8 + 4$ $9 + 4$ $9 + 9$ $11 - 7$ $12 - 3$

$6 - 1$ $4 + 9$ $3 + 2$

Note for parent: This activity gives practice in adding and taking away numbers to 20.

Quick quiz

Write the numbers to complete these adding chains.

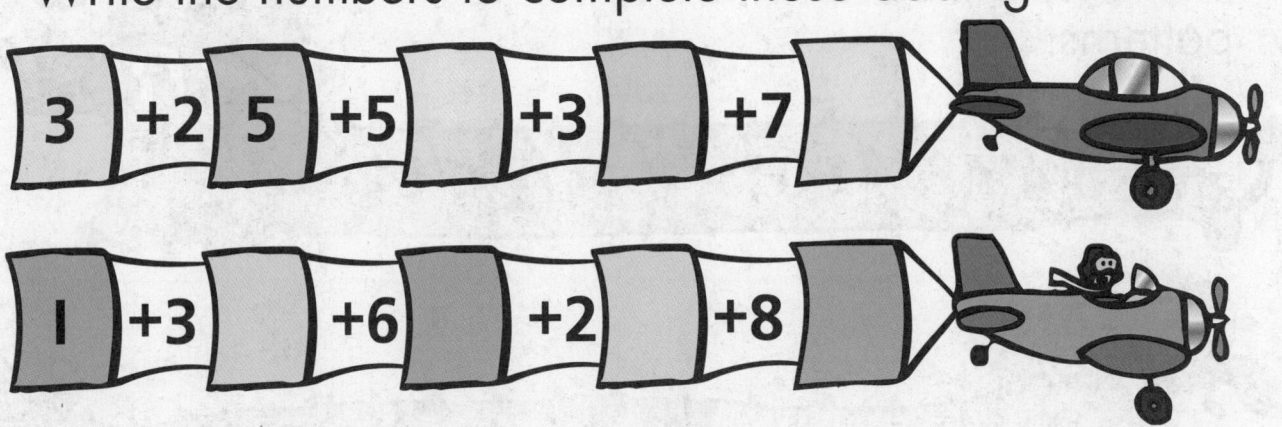

Circle the odd one out in each set.

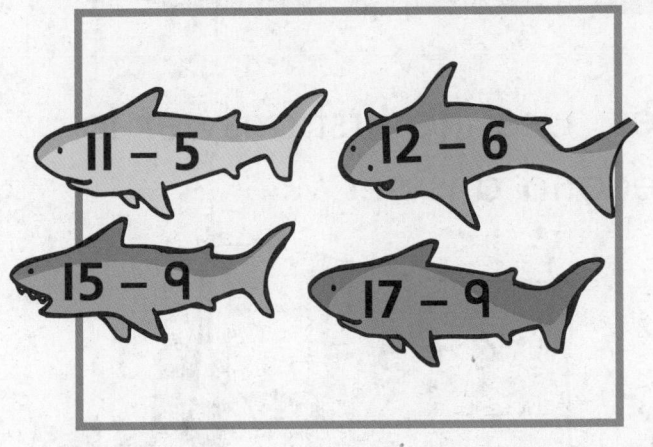

Write the change from 20p for each of these.

change: ⬜ p

change: ⬜ p

change: ⬜ p

Note for parent: This page is another chance to revise some of the learning so far.

27

Large numbers

Write the missing numbers in these patterns.

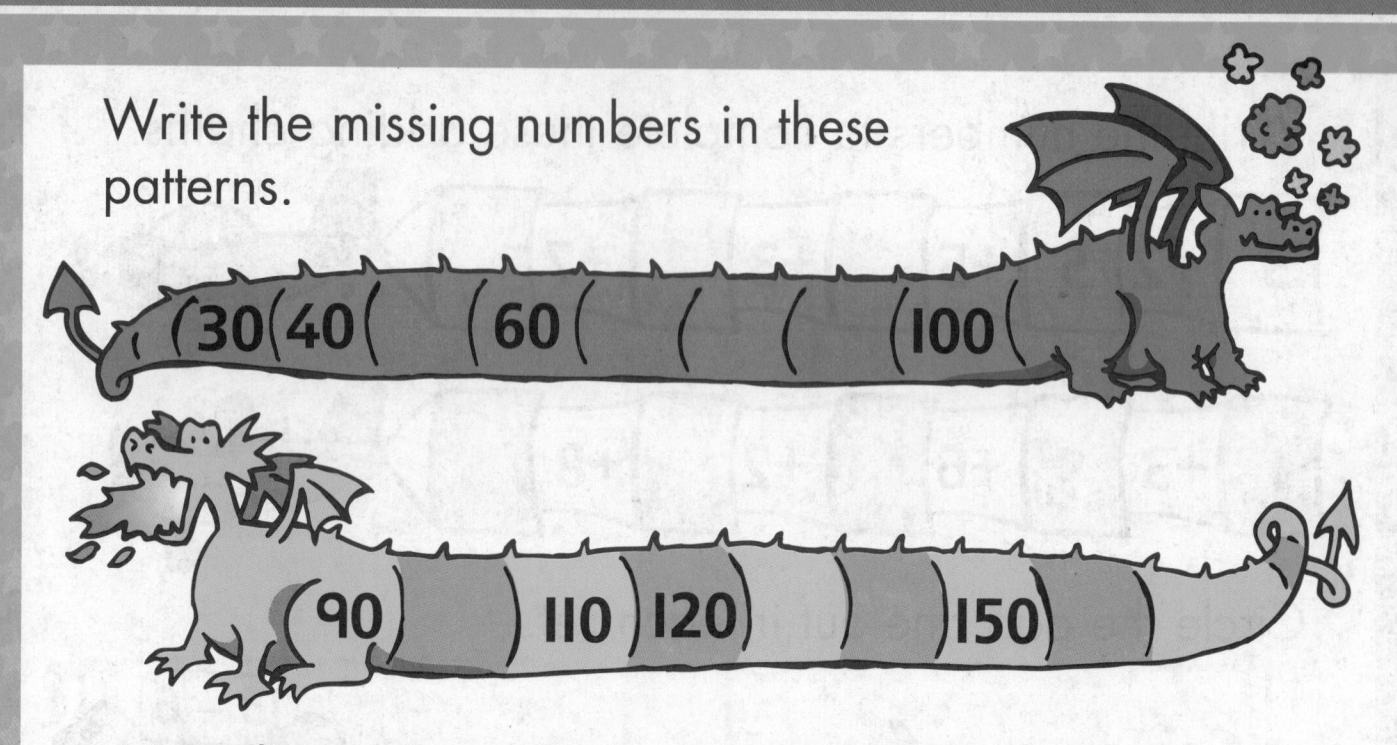

((30(40((60 ((((100 (

(90) 110)120 ( ) (150 ( )

Write the totals in the boxes. Use the first answer to help you to work out the second answer.

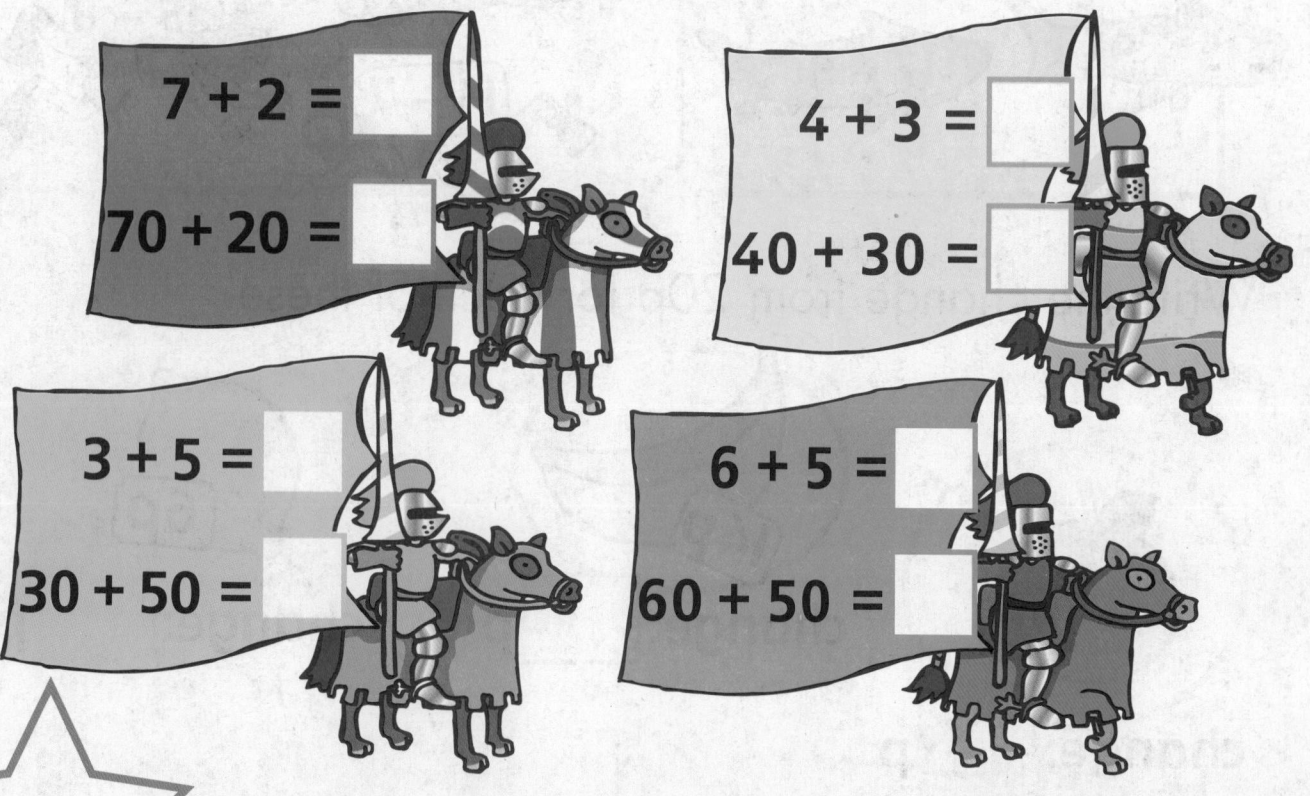

7 + 2 = ☐

70 + 20 = ☐

4 + 3 = ☐

40 + 30 = ☐

3 + 5 = ☐

30 + 50 = ☐

6 + 5 = ☐

60 + 50 = ☐

Note for parent: This activity gives practice in adding multiples of 10.

Draw a line to match each dragon to the correct cave.

120

110

90 + 60 =

70 + 70 =

50 + 80 =

90

150

50 + 70 =

140

60 + 30 =

130

70 + 40 =

Subtract large numbers

Complete these number trails.

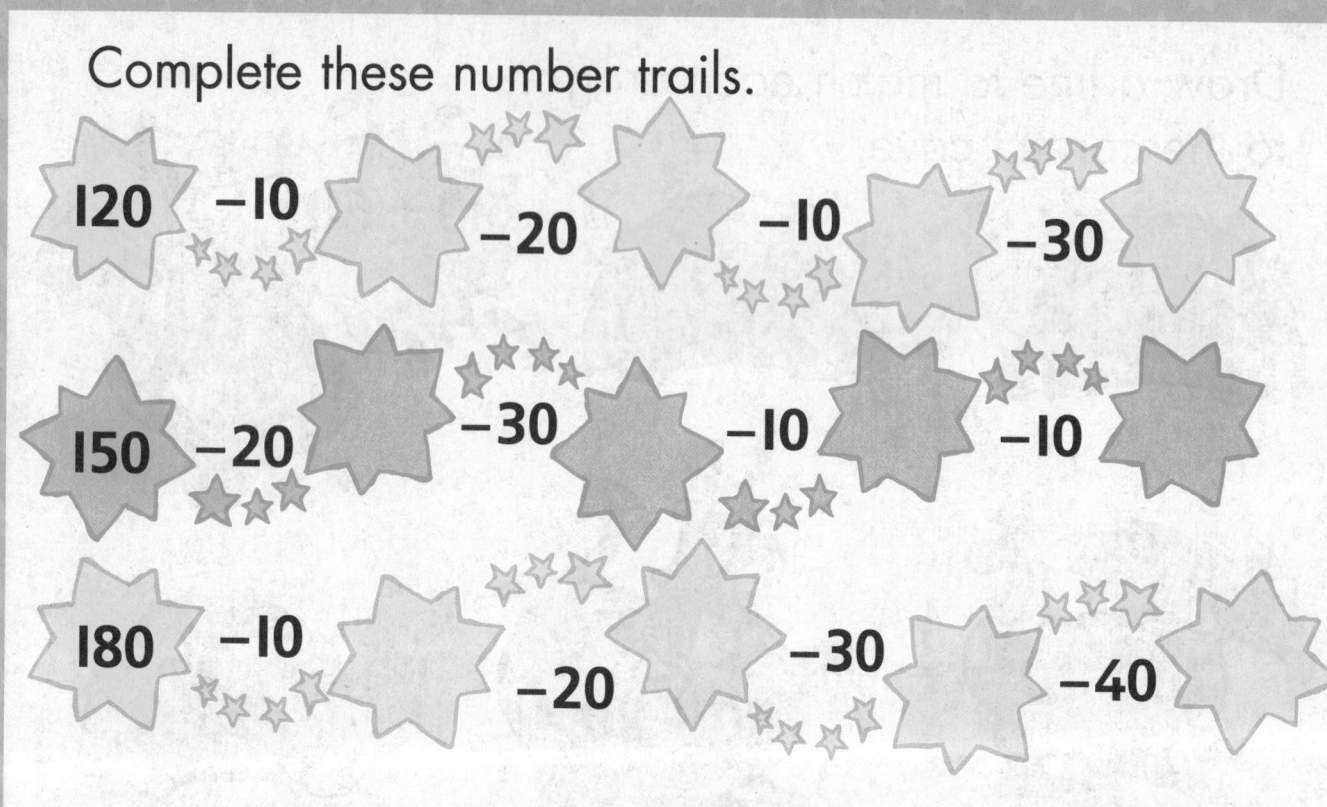

120 −10 ___ −20 ___ −10 ___ −30 ___

150 −20 ___ −30 ___ −10 ___ −10 ___

180 −10 ___ −20 ___ −30 ___ −40 ___

Answer these sums. Use the first answer to help you work out the second answer.

8 − 3 = ___
80 − 30 = ___

7 − 4 = ___
70 − 40 = ___

15 − 8 = ___
150 − 80 = ___

9 − 5 = ___
90 − 50 = ___

12 − 7 = ___
120 − 70 = ___

14 − 6 = ___
140 − 60 = ___

Note for parent: This activity gives practice in subtracting multiples of 10. Your child may need some extra support with the three-digit numbers.

Colour the flying saucers that have the same answer.
Use a different colour for each matching pair.

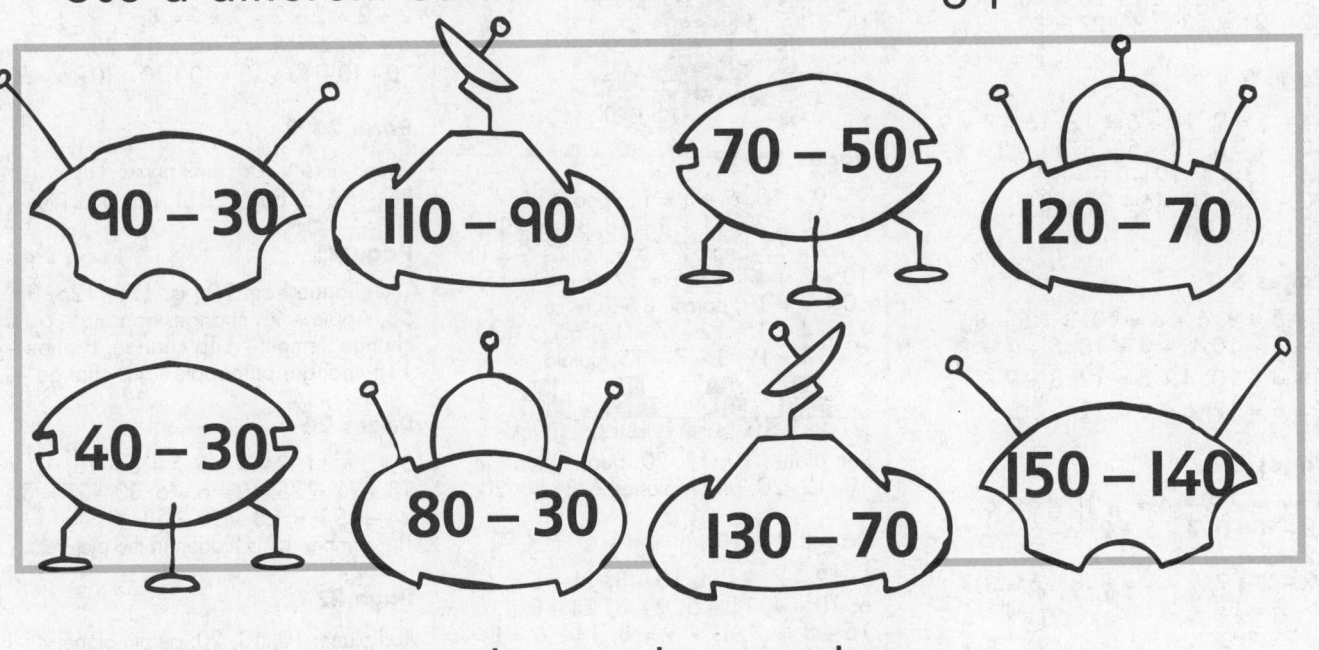

Draw lines to join the numbers with a
difference of 50.

Answers

Page 4

8 + 4 = 12, 7 + 7 = 14.
9 + 6 = 15, 13 + 4 = 17,
15 + 5 = 20, 11 + 10 = 21,
16 + 13 = 29, 20 + 20 = 40,
32 + 21 = 53, 55 + 27 = 82.

Page 5

14 − 5 = 9, 18 − 6 = 12, 16 − 7 = 9.
10 − 4 = 6, 13 − 5 = 8, 11 − 3 = 8,
14 − 13 = 1, 19 − 11 = 8,
20 − 10 = 10, 46 − 25 = 21,
63 − 37 = 26.

Pages 6–7

4 + 5 = 9, 6 + 4 = 10, 3 + 5 = 8,
5 + 5 = 10. 6 + 4 = 10, 5 + 7 = 12,
7 + 3 = 10. 4 + 8 = 12, 3 + 9 = 12,
7 + 5 = 12, 6 + 6 = 12.

Pages 8–9

6 − 4 = 2, 9 − 4 = 5, 10 − 4 = 6,
12 − 4 = 8, 7 − 5 = 2, 9 − 5 = 4,
12 − 5 = 7, 11 − 5 = 6.
12 − 3 = 9, 9 − 1 = 8, 8 − 5 = 3,
3 − 2 = 1.

Pages 10–11

4 + 7 = 11, 8 + 5 = 13, 6 + 9 = 15.
+ 9 machine: 7 + 9 = 16, 4 + 9 = 13,
8 + 9 = 17, 5 + 9 = 14, 9 + 9 = 18.
− 7 machine: 12 − 7 = 5, 9 − 7 = 2,
15 − 7 = 8, 13 − 7 = 6, 10 − 7 = 3.
− 9 machine: 11 − 9 = 2, 14 − 9 = 5,
12 − 9 = 3, 18 − 9 = 9, 16 − 9 = 7.

Pages 12–13

The difference between 3 and 7 is 4.
The difference between 5 and 11 is 6.
The difference between 6 and 11 is 5.
The difference between 9 and 4 is 5.
The difference between 12 and 15 is 3.

Yellow submarine: 9; red submarine:
5 or 15; purple submarine: 8; blue
submarine: 4 or 14.

Page 14

Total of 9: 4 + 5, 7 + 2, 6 + 3, 8 + 1.
Total of 12: 4 + 8, 5 + 7, 6 + 6, 9 + 3.

Page 15

5 + 5 = 10. 6 − 4 = 2, 10 − 4 = 6.

Pages 16–17

9 + 9 = 18, 6 + 5 = 11, pea.
12 + 8 = 20, 11 + 7 = 18, 8 + 3 = 11,
7 + 7 = 14, bean. 7 + 5 = 12, 2 + 9 = 11,
10 + 7 = 17, 8 + 9 = 17, 9 + 6 = 15,
10 + 9 = 19, carrot. 8 + 8 = 16,
11 + 4 = 15, 12 + 7 = 19, 6 + 5 = 11,
5 + 14 = 19, 8 + 7 = 15, potato.

Red plane: 10, 13, 20; purple plane: 4,
10, 12, 20; green plane: 7, 8, 14, 20.

Pages 18–19

5: 12 − 7, 9 − 4, 13 − 8, 11 − 6.
6: 10 − 4, 11 − 5, 9 − 3, 14 − 8.
15 − 8 = 7, 17 − 9 = 8, 14 − 6 = 8,
13 − 9 = 4, 11 − 4 = 7, 12 − 8 = 4.
The odd ones out are: top left: 18 − 9,
top right: 14 − 8, centre: 17 − 9.
13 − 9 and 11 − 7, 14 − 8 and
12 − 6, 15 − 8 and 13 − 6.

Pages 20–21

14 − 7 = seven, 11 − 6 = five,
13 − 7 = six, 17 − 5 = twelve,
13 − 5 = eight, 16 − 15 = one,
16 − 7 = nine.
Mystery number = sixteen.
Purple answers: 9 − 4 = 5, 8 − 7 = 1,
11 − 6 = 5, 7 − 5 = 2, 10 − 7 = 3.
Orange answers: 12 − 6 = 6,
7 − 4 = 3, 15 − 10 = 5, 9 − 6 = 3,
11 − 4 = 7. Green answers: 8 − 4 = 4,
13 − 8 = 5, 6 − 2 = 4, 10 − 5 = 5,
14 − 7 = 7. Blue see-saw: 9 and 5;
green see-saw: 8 and 8; yellow see-
saw: 7 and 13. Dog: 11, 5; pig: 17,
13, 6; hen: 18, 15, 7.

Page 22

4 + 4 = 8, 6 + 6 = 12, 3 + 3 = 6,
5 + 5 = 10, 8 + 8 = 16, 2 + 2 = 4,
13 + 13 = 26, 10 + 10 = 20, 19 + 19 = 38.
3 + 4 = 7, 10 + 9 = 19, 5 + 6 = 11,
5 + 4 = 9, 8 + 9 = 17, 6 + 7 = 13,
8 + 7 = 15.

Pages 23

5 + 5 + 5 = 15, 10 + 10 + 10 = 30.
5 + 5 + 5 = 5 × 3 + 15.
10 + 10 + 10 = 10 × 3 = 30.
2 + 2 + 2 + 2 = 2 × 4 = 8.
5 + 5 + 5 + 5 + 5 = 5 × 5 = 25.
10 + 10 + 10 + 10 + 10 + 10 = 10 × 6 = 60.

Page 24

Green purse: 20p; pink purse: 18p.
Box 1: £12; box 2: £11; box 3: £16.

Page 25

The change from 20p is: 13p, 12p, 8p,
5p. Apple – 9p change, banana – 6p
change, lemon – 14p change, orange –
11p change, pineapple – 4p change.

Pages 26

8 + 3 = 11, 9 − 4 = 5, 7 + 6 = 13,
13 + 12 = 25, 12 − 6 = 6, 30 − 27 = 3,
24 − 15 = 9, 23 + 30 = 53.
The number 15 is hidden in the picture.

Page 27

Red plane: 10, 13, 20; purple plane: 4,
10, 12, 20. Odd ones out: left: 17 − 9;
right: 18 − 9. Apple – 9p change, banana
– 6p change, lemon – 14p change.

Page 28-29

Missing numbers: red dragon: 50, 70,
80, 90, 110; green dragon: 100, 130,
140, 160, 170.
7 + 2 = 9, 70 + 20 = 90; 4 + 3 = 7,
40 + 30 = 70; 3 + 5 = 8,
30 + 50 = 80; 6 + 5 = 11,
60 + 50 = 110.
90 + 60 = 150, 70 + 70 = 140,
50 + 80 = 130, 50 + 70 = 120,
60 + 30 = 90, 70 + 40 = 110.

Pages 30–31

Missing numbers: top: 110, 90, 80, 50;
middle: 130, 100, 90, 80; bottom: 170,
150, 120, 80. 8 − 3 = 5, 80 − 30 = 50;
7 − 4 = 3, 70 − 40 = 30; 15 − 8 = 7,
150 − 80 = 70; 9 − 5 = 4, 90 − 50 = 40;
12 − 7 = 5, 120 − 70 = 50; 14 − 6 = 8,
140 − 60 = 80.

110 and 60, 40 and 90, 130 and 80,
170 and 120.